FRANZ SCH[

MASS No. 6

E♭ major / Es-Dur / Mi♭ majeur
for 5 Solo Voices, Chorus and Orchestra
für 5 Solostimmen, Chor und Orchester
D 950

Edited by / Herausgegeben von
Hermann Grabner

Ernst Eulenburg Ltd

London · Mainz · Madrid · New York · Paris · Tokyo · Toronto · Zürich

Ernst Eulenburg Ltd
48 Great Marlborough Street
London W1V 2BN

K Y R I E

Seigneur, ayez pitié de nous. Christ, ayez pitié de nous.	Kyrie eleison. Christe eleison.	Lord, have mercy upon us Christ, have mercy upon us.

G L O R I A

Gloire à Dieu au plus haut des cieux, et paix sur terre aux hommes de bonne volonté.

Gloria in excelsis Deo, et in terra pax hominibus bonæ voluntatis.

Glory be to God on high, and on earth peace, good will towards men.

Nous vous louons,

Nous vous bénissons,

Nous vous adorons,

Nous vous glorifions,

Laudamus te,

Benedicimus te,

Adoramus te,

Glorificamus te,

We praise Thee,

We bless Thee,

We adore Thee,

We glorify Thee,

Nous vous rendons grâces à cause de votre grande gloire.

Gratias agimus tibi propter magnam gloriam tuam.

We give thanks to Thee for Thy great glory.

Seigneur Dieu,Roi du ciel ô Dieu Père tout-puissant. Seigneur Jésus Christ, Fils unique de Dieu, Seigneur Dieu, Agneau de Dieu, Fils du Père.

Domine Deus, Rex cœlestis, Deus Pater omnipotens. Domine fili unigenite, Jesu Christe, Domine Deus, Agnus dei, Filius Patris.

O Lord God, heavenly king, God the Father Almighty. O Lord, the only begotten Son Jesus Christ, O Lord God,Lamb of God, Son of the Father.

Vous qui effacez les péchés du monde, ayez pitié de nous. Vous qui effacez les péchés du monde, recevez notre prière.

Qui tollis peccata mundi, miserere nobis. Qui tollis peccata mundi, suscipe deprecationem nostram.

Thou that takest away the sins of the world, have mercy upon us. Thou that takest away the sins of the world, receive our prayer.

Vous qui êtes assis à la droite du Père, ayez pitié de nous.

Qui sedes ad dexteram Patris, miserere nobis.

Thou that sittest at the right hand of the Father, have mercy upon us.

Car vous êtes le seul Saint le seul Seigneur, le seul Très Haut, ô Jésus Christ, avec le Saint Esprit, dans la gloire de Dieu le Père. Ainsi soit-il.

Quoniam tu solus sanctus, tu solus Dominus, tu solus altissimus, Jesu Christe, cum Sancto Spiritu in gloria Dei Patris. Amen.

For Thou only art holy; Thou only art the Lord; Thou only, O Christ, with the Holy Ghost, art most high in the glory of God the Father. Amen.

IV

C R E D O

Je crois en un seul Dieu, Père tout-puissant, créateur du ciel et de la terre, de toutes les choses visibles et invisibles.

Et en un seul Seigneur, Jésus-Christ, Fils unique de Dieu, né du Père avant tous les siècles.

Dieu de Dieu, lumière de lumière, vrai Dieu de vrai Dieu. Engendré, non créé, consubstantiel au Père, par qui tout a été fait. Qui pour nous, hommes, et pour notre salut, est descendu des cieux.

Qui s'est incarné par l'opération du Saint-Esprit, en la Vierge Marie ET S'EST FAIT HOMME.

Qui a été crucifié pour nous, a souffert sous Ponce Pilate et a été enseveli.

Qui est ressuscité le troisième jour, selon les Ecritures. Qui est monté au ciel, est assis à la droite du Père. Qui viendra de nouveau dans la gloire pour juger les vivants et les morts, et dont le règne n'aura point de fin.

Et je crois au Saint-Esprit, Seigneur et auteur de la vie, qui procède du Père et du Fils. Qui est adoré et glorifié conjointement avec le Père et le Fils; qui a parlé par les Prophètes.

Credo in unum Deum, patrem omnipotentem, factorem cœli et terræ, visibilium omnium et invisibilium.

Et in unum Dominum, Jesum Christum, Filium Dei unigenitum, et ex Patre natum ante omnia sæcula.

Deum de Deo, lumen de lumine, Deum verum de Deo vero. Genitum, non factum, consubstantialem Patri, per quem omnia facta sunt. Qui propter nos homines et propter nostram salutem, descendit de cœlis.

Et incarnatus est de Spiritu Sancto ex Maria Virgine ET HOMO FACTUS EST.

Crucifixus etiam pro nobis, sub Pontio Pilato passus et sepultus est.

Et resurrexit tertia die, secundum Scripturas; et ascendit in cœlum; sedet ad dexteram Patris, et iterum venturus est cum gloria judicare vivos et mortuos, cujus regni non erit finis.

Et in spiritum Sanctum, Dominum et vivificantem, qui ex Patre Filioque procedit, qui cum Patre et Filio simul adoratur, et conglorificatur; qui locutus est per prophetas.

I believe in one God the Father Almighty, Maker of heaven and earth, and of all things visible and invisible.

And in one Lord Jesus Christ, the only-begotten Son of God, begotten of his Father before all worlds.

God of God, Light of Light, very God of very God begotten, not made, being of one substance with the Father, by whom all things are made: who for us men, and for our salvation came down from heaven.

And was incarnate by the Holy Ghost of the Virgin Mary, AND WAS MADE MAN.

And was crucified also for us under Pontius Pilate. He suffered and was buried

And the third day he rose again according to Scriptures, and ascended into heaven, and sitteth on the right hand of the Father. And He shall come again with glory to judge both the quick and the dead: whose kingdom shall have no end.

And I believe in the Holy Ghost, the Lord and Giver of Life, Who proceedeth from the Father and the Son, Who with the Father and the Son together is worshipped and glorified, who spake by the Prophets.

Je crois l'Eglise, Une, Sainte, Catholique et Apostolique. Je confesse un seul baptême pour la rémission des péchés. Et j'attends la résurrection des morts et la vie du siècle à venir. Ainsi soit-il.

Et in unam, sanctam, catholicam et apostolicam Ecclesiam, Confiteor unum baptisma in remissionem peccatorum, et expecto resurrectionem mortuorum, et vitam venturi sæculi. Amen.

And I believe one Catholic and Apostolic Church. I acknowledge one Baptism for the remission of sins. And I look for the resurrection of the dead, and the life everlasting of the world to come. Amen.

S A N C T U S

Saint est le Seigneur, le Dieu des armées.

Sanctus Dominus Deus Sabaoth.

Holy, Lord God of Sabaoth.

Les cieux et la terre sont pleins de votre gloire.

Pleni sunt cœli et terra gloria tua.

Heaven and earth are full of Thy glory.

Hosanna au plus haut des cieux.

Hosanna in excelsis.

Hosanna in the highest.

Béni soit celui qui vient au nom du Seigneur.

Benedictus qui venit in nomine Domini.

Blessed is he that cometh in the name of the Lord.

Hosanna au plus haut des cieux.

Hosanna in excelsis.

Hosanna in the highest.

A G N U S   D E I

Agneau de Dieu qui effacez les péchés du monde, ayez pitié de nous.

Agnus Dei qui tollis peccata mundi, miserere nobis.

O Lamb of God, that takest away the sins of the world, have mercy upon us.

Agneau de Dieu qui effacez les péchés du monde, donnez-nous la paix.

Agnus Dei qui tollis peccata mundi, dona nobis pacem.

O Lamb of God that takest away the sins of the world, grant us Thy peace.

FRANZ SCHUBERT

Messe Nr. VI in Es-Dur

Komponiert im Sommer 1828 in Wien
Erstaufführung am 15. November 1829 in Wien in der Pfarrkirche
Maria Trost nach dem Manuskript
Im Druck erschienen im Dezember 1865 und Januar 1866
bei J. Rieter-Biedermann, Leipzig

Übersichtliche Darstellung der einzelnen Teile:

I. KYRIE

Andante con moto, quasi allegretto für Chor und Orchester
Es-Dur, $^8/_4$ . . . . Seite 1

Kyrie eleison! Christe eleison! Kyrie eleison!	Herr, erbarme dich! Christe, erbarme dich! Herr, erbarme dich!

II. GLORIA

a) Allegro moderato e maestoso für Chor und Orchester, B-Dur, $^4/_4$ Seite 26

Gloria in excelsis Deo et in terra pax hominibus bonæ voluntatis.	Ehre sei Gott in der Höhe, Friede auf Erden und den Menschen ein Wohlgefallen.
Laudamus te, benedicimus te, adoramus te, glorificamus te. Gratias agimus tibi propter magnam gloriam tuam.	Wir loben dich, wir verherrlichen dich, wir beten dich an, wir preisen dich. Wir danken dir um deines großen Ruhmes willen.

b) Andante con moto für Chor und Orchester, G-Moll, $^8/_4$ . . . Seite 49

Domine Deus, rex cœlestis, Deus pater omnipotens. Domine Fili unigenite, Jesu Christe Domine Deus, agnus Dei, Filius Patris.	Herr, unser Gott, König des Himmels, Gott Vater, Allmächtiger. Herr, des Vaters eingeborner Sohn, Jesus Christus, Herr, unser Gott, Lamm Gottes, Sohn des Vaters.
Qui tollis peccata mundi, miserere nobis. Qui tollis peccata mundi, suscipe deprecationem nostram. Qui sedes ad dexteram Patris, miserere nobis.	Der du trägst die Sünden der Welt, erbarme dich unser, der du trägst die Sünden der Welt, erhöre unser Flehen! Der du sitzest zur Rechten des Vaters, erbarme dich unser!

c) Tempo I für Chor und Orchester, B-Dur, $^4/_4$ . . . . Seite 58

Quoniam tu solus sanctus Dominus, tu solus altissimus.	Denn du allein bist heilig, o Herr, du allein bist der Höchste.

| Cum sancto spiritu in gloria Dei Patris, Amen. | Mit dem heiligen Geiste in der Herrlichkeit Gottes des Vaters. |

III. CREDO

| Credo in unum Deum, factorem cœli et terræ, visibilium omnium ét invisibilium, et in unum Dominum Jesum Christum, Filium Dei unige-nitum, et ex patre natum atne omnia sæcula, Deum de Deo, lumen de lumine, Deum verum de Deo vero, genitum, non factum, consubstan-tialem Patri, per quem omnia facta sunt; qui propter nos homines et propter nostram salutem descendit de cœlis. | Ich glaube an einen einigen Gott, Schöpfer Himmels und der Erden, aller sichtbaren und unsichtbaren Dinge, und an den einigen Herrn Jesum Christum, Gottes eingebo-renen Sohn, aus dem Vater geboren vor allen Zeiten; Gott von Gott, Licht von Licht, wahrer Gott vom wahren Gott, gezeugt, nicht ge-schaffen, gleichen Wesens mit dem Vater, durch den alles erschaffen worden ist, der für uns Menschen und für unser Heil herabstieg vom Himmel. |

| Et incarnatus est de spiritu sancto, ex Maria virgine et homo factus est, | Und er ward empfangen vom heiligen Geiste, geboren von der Jungfrau Maria und ist Mensch ge-worden, |
| Crucificus etiam pro nobis sub Pontio Pilato, passus et sepultus est. | Er wurde gekreuzigt auch für uns unter Pontius Pilatus, litt und ward begraben, |

| Et resurrexit tertia die secundum scripturas et ascendit in cœlum, sedet ad dexteram Dei Patris, et iterum venturus est cum gloria judicare vivos et mortuos, cujus regni non erit finis. | Und ist wieder auferstanden am dritten Tage, wie da geschrieben steht, und ist aufgefahren gen Him-mel, wo er sitzt zur Rechten Gottes des Vaters. Und von dannen wird er wieder kommen in Herrlichkeit, zu richten die Lebendigen und die Toten, und sein Reich wird kein Ende haben. |

Et in spiritum sanctum Dominum et vivificantem, qui ex Patre filioque procedit, qui cum Patre et Filio simul adoratur et conglorificatur, qui locutus est per Prophetas.

Et in unam sanctam catholicam et apostolicam ecclesiam. Confiteor unum baptisma in remissionem peccatorum. Et expecto resurrectionem mortuorum. Et vitam venturi sæculi, Amen.

Und (ich glaube) an den heiligen Geist, der Herr ist und Leben gibt, der aus dem Vater und dem Sohne zugleich hervorgeht, der mit dem Vater und dem Sohne zugleich angebetet und verehrt wird, der geredet hat durch die Propheten.

Und (ich glaube) an eine heilige allgemeine und apostolische Kirche. Ich bekenne eine Taufe zur Vergebung der Sünden. Und ich erwarte die Auferstehung der Toten. Und ein zukünftiges ewiges Leben, Amen.

IV. SANCTUS

Sanctus Dominus Deus Sabaoth. Pleni sunt cœli et terra gloria ejus.

Heilig ist der Herr Zebaoth. Voll sind Himmel und Erde von seinem Ruhm.

Osanna in excelsis!

Hosanna in der Höhe!

V. BENEDICTUS

Benedictus qui venit in nomine Domini! Osanna in excelsis Deo!

Hochgelobt sei, der da kommt im Namen des Herrn. Hosanna in der Höhe!

VI. AGNUS DEI

Agnus Dei, qui tollis peccata mundi, miserere nobis.

Christe, du Lamm Gottes, der du trägst die Sünden der Welt, erbarme dich unser.

Dona nobis pacem!

Gib uns Frieden!

Agnus Dei, qui tollis peccata mundi, miserere nobis.

Christe, du Lamm Gottes, der du trägst die Sünden der Welt, erbarme dich unser.

Dona nobis pacem!

Gib uns Frieden!

INTRODUCTION

Just ·as the Schubert Symphonies form the link between the classical and new romantic schools, so, in the world of sacred music, the master carries on the development towards the Mass by Anton Bruckner. The six Masses of Schubert like his Symphonies are modelled after the form of Haydn and Mozart, but enriched by greater power of expression and wealth of melody and harmony.

It must be admitted that the union of a romantic musical style with religious words does not always produce ideal results, and the lyrical quality of Schubert's genius, so well-adapted to the Song form, can hardly cope with the dramatic power of the text, every word of which demands greater force. Likewise, the text is ill-suited to the graceful play of fancy which Schubert reveals, so near to the spirit of the age and the classical Symphonic and Sonata forms.

From the sublime strength of the old Missa, masters such as Palestrina, Orlando di Lasso, Dufay, Okeghem and Josquin Després drew their powerful works, the "Choral Symphony" of their time. Bach, in a purely Protestant spirit, approached his text in a quite different manner when he wrote his gigantic B minor Mass, the last link in a long chain of polyphonic music.

No musical form demands polyphony so much as the Mass; it is it's very essence, required by the text, which is not content with the self-sufficing, single-voiced presentation of accompanied melody. A deeper reason lies in this desire for all voices to take part; it is as though none can refrain from joining in the praise of the Creator, as though all were impelled to crave His mercy, to cry forth Sanctus and

Hosanna, to step before His throne, steadfast in faith, and humbly bow down before the Son of God, who bore the sins of the world.

It was by no mere chance that polyphonic music reached it's zenith in an age when the Mass was considered the highest form of musical expression. Beethoven's mighty genius demanded it and informed it with a new spirit. He employed polyphony in his great work, the "Missa solemnis" as a contrast to moments of subjective feeling, which he treated with solo voices. His creative faculty grasped the true meaning and importance of the old polyphonic Mass with extraordinary ease. Through it he cultivated a new sacred style, which bursts the bonds of the usual liturgical Mass, and must be regarded as an off-shoot from the main branch of religious music.

Schubert, though his genius was naturally lyrical, was also well aware of the immense effects to be obtained by treating choral masses in a polyphonic manner. In his E flat major Mass both the Gloria and the Credo terminate in powerful fugues. Even the Sanctus is in Fugato form, whilst the Agnus Dei is treated with contrapuntal detail. These portions, with their powerful climaxes form the most important features of the work. But where the Chorus is treated homophonically, when his lyrical feeling becomes predominant, Schubert loses his hold over the holy text. The Kyrie of this Mass, for instance, flows on in the true Schubertian melodic spirit, delightful, considered as pure music, but bearing no relation to the deep meaning in the words. There is no hint here of a despairing cry for mercy, and of humble prayer, which are expressed so wonderfully in Bach's B minor Mass.

Neither do we receive the impression of subjectivity which informs Beethoven's "Missa solemnis", but simply the spinning-out of romantic melody, devoted almost entirely to the upper voices.

It is in the Credo, "Et incarnatus est" (page 100) given to two Tenors and Soprano solo, in the Quartet solo of the Benedictus (page 175) and finally the "Dona nobis pacem" of the Agnus Dei (Solo Quartet and Chorus) that Schubert pours forth his richest stream of inspiration. The whole work indeed is the apotheosis of beautiful sound, typically romantic in quality. The brass instruments, imposing in number for those days (2 Trumpets, 2 Horns and 3 Trombones) are well handled as a separate body and form a fine contrast to the group of wood-wind (2 Oboes, 2 Clarinets, 2 Bassoons), on one hand, and the Strings on the other. The fourth group, the Chorus, gains effects which the composer had not reached hitherto. Note, for instance, the Andante con moto of the Gloria: „Domine Deus, agnus Dei, qui tollis peccata mundi", where the Tenors and Bass in octaves join the fortissimo trombone theme in unison, the effect of which is heightened by the following Chorus, sung pianissimo. The desire for musical tone-painting is here revealed, the composer distributing harmonic colour which in his day must have had startling effect, and which is somewhat arresting even at the present time. Note for instance the related harmonies of A flat major and C flat major (bar 133 of the Kyrie) and the contrasting keys of E flat major, B minor and G minor at the beginning of the Sanctus.

It we discover a typically romantic bent in the inclination for tone-painting, we also become aware of a desire for the expansion of absolute instrumental form though not prompted by the development of the text; the recurrence of moods, for instance, which have already passsed, such as the repitition of the whole of the "Incarnatus" and "Crucifixus" (page 112 etc.) after the word "Passus et sepultus est". Further capricious handling of the text is shown in the omission of the words "patrem omnipotentem" at the beginning of the Credo or the second "Jesu Christe" in the Gloria and the prolongation of the "Osanna in excelsis" by the word "Deo".

Schubert's E flat major Mass may be considered a work which does not express the innermost feeling of the text, as do the Masses of Bach and Beethoven, but which delivers a message of piety in naive and genial manner, and exhibits the warm and ingenuous spirit for which Schubert's imperishable music is so greatly loved.

Hermann Grabner.

EINFÜHRUNG

Wie Schubert für die symphonische Musik das Bindeglied zwischen dem klassischen und neuromantischen Stil darstellt, so weist er auf dem Gebiet der Kirchenmusik der Entwicklung den Weg bis zur Messe Anton Bruckners. Wie in seinen Symphonien lehnt er sich auch in seinen sechs Messen zunächst an die Form Haydns und Mozarts an, die er erweitert und durch die Ausdruckskraft seiner Harmonik und Melodik bereichert.

Freilich ist, bei reiner Betrachtung der Verknüpfungsmöglichkeit des romantischen Stiles mit dem Messetext, von vornherein ein Zwiespalt in der Art der musikalischen Gestaltung festgelegt. Das Lyrische, Liedmäßige der Schubertschen Muse fügt sich nur schwer in die dramatische Wucht und Größe jenes Textes, bei dem jedes Wort nach stärkster Gestaltung ringt. Ebensowenig vermag dieser Text der klassischen Vorliebe für das feine, spielerische und graziöse Geschehen entgegenzukommen, wie wir es in der klassischen Sonate und Symphonie in so vollendeter Weise, ganz dem Geist der Zeit und des klassischen Kunstwerkes entsprechend, finden.

Ganz aus dem innersten Wesen jener gewaltigen Kräfte, die sich in der erhabenen Liturgie der alten Missa vereint finden, schufen die Meister der niederländischen Kunst, D u f a y , O k e g h e m , J o s q u i n D e s p r é s , schufen P a l e s t r i n a und O r l a n d o   d i   L a s s o ihre gewaltigen Messen, die „Chorsymphonien" ihrer Zeit.

Wie anders nahte sich diesem Text ein J. S. B a c h , der ganz aus protestantischem Geiste heraus, als ein Schlußstein einer zu höchster Entfaltung gelangenden polyphonen Epoche, das zyklopische Riesenwerk seiner H-Moll-Messe schrieb.

Keine Form drängt so zur Polyphonie wie die der Messe. Man könnte ruhig sagen: D a s   m u s i k a l i s c h e   W e s e n   d e r   M e s s e i s t   P o l y p,h o n i e , ihr Text verlangt nach Vielstimmigkeit, wendet sich bewußt ab von der monodischen Gestaltung der begleiteten, selbstherrlichen Melodie. Ein tieferer Sinn liegt in diesem Verlangen nach Teilnahme a l l e r Stimmen an der Melodie: Es ist, als ob keine Stimme zurückstehen möchte, mit der ganzen Kraft ihrer aus dem Innersten strömenden Sangesweise den Schöpfer zu preisen, sein Erbarmen herabzuflehen, seinen Ruhm zu verkünden, mit dem Bekenntnis des Glaubens vor seinen Thron zu treten, ihm ein Sanctus und Hosanna entgegenzujubeln und sich in tiefster Demut vor dem Lamm Gottes, welches die Sünden der Welt trägt, zu verneigen.

Es ist kein Zufall, daß zur Zeit, als die Form der Messe für den Menschen das Herrlichste war, was es in Töne zu kleiden gab, die Polyphonie ihre höchste Blüte entfaltete. Da bedurfte es schon des übermächtigen Genies Beethovens, um aus dem Wesen der klassischen Musik heraus diese Kunstform mit neuem Geiste zu erfüllen. Er verpflanzte in das Riesenwerk seiner Missa solemnis das Moment des subjektiven Empfindens, das er in solistischen Partien zum Ausdruck brachte und den chorischen Massenwirkungen gegenüberstellte. Die Errungenschaften seiner Symphonie aber übertrug er, als der absoluten Musik angehörig, nur insoweit auf die Gestaltung seiner Messe, als sie geeignet erschienen, den Geist des gesungenen Wortes durch die Macht seiner Instrumentalsprache zu verklären. Mit außerordentlicher Klarheit griff sein schöpferischer Geist die polyphone Idee der alten Messe auf und erreichte damit die höchste Vollkommenheit eines neuen kirchlichen Stiles, der freilich in seinen übermächtigen Dimensionen den Rahmen der üblichen liturgischen Messe sprengt und als ein von der kirchlichen Kultushandlung Losgelöstes betrachtet sein will.

Auch Schubert, obwohl seiner lyrischen Veranlagung nach homophon eingestellt, war sich der Kräfte wohl bewußt, welche aus der polyphonen Gestaltung der Chorsätze Steigerungen ungeahnter Mächtigkeit zu entfalten imstande sind. In seiner Es-Dur-Messe werden Glória und Credo durch mächtige Fugen mit Engführungen gekrönt. Auch das Sanctus läuft in ein kräftig bewegtes Fugato aus, und namentlich das Agnus Dei zeigt eine fein verästelte Kontrapunktik, die deutlich Zeugnis ablegt von dem kontrapunktischen Instinkt, von dem sich Schubert bei der Wahl dieses (an das Lied „Der Doppelgänger" gemahnenden) Themas leiten ließ. In diesen Partien liegen denn auch die Höhepunkte des Werkes und ein kräftig männlicher Zug führt zu Steigerungen gewaltiger Wirkung. Wo dagegen der Chor homophon gestaltet ist, wo das lyrische Element die Oberhand gewinnt und den Messetext in einer ihm nicht entsprechenden. weichen Gefühlseligkeit zu gestalten sucht, vermissen wir die kraftvolle Interpretation der heiligen Worte. So fließt z. B. das Kyrie dieser Messe in einer, von echt Schubertschem Geiste getragenen Melodie dahin, die, rein musikalisch genommen, das Entzücken jedes Musikfreundes hervorrufen wird, während sie einen Zusammenhang mit der Tiefe der Worte nicht erkennen läßt. Es ist kein von tiefster Zerknirschung durchdrungenes Flehen um Erbarmen, das bald in demütigem Stammeln, bald in nach Erlösung aufschreienden Gebeten zum Himmel dringen will, wie wir es in Bachs H-Moll-Messe in höchster Vollendung

sehen. Es ist auch nicht die ausdruckserfüllte Subjektivierung der Beethovenschen Missa, sondern eine aus der Klangwelt der Romantik erschaute Fortspinnung einer fast ausschließlich in der Oberstimme festgehaltenen Melodie. Diese objektivierende Betrachtungsweise Schuberts wird auch durch die vorübergehende solistische Betätigung des Vokalen nicht berührt. Es sind dies zunächst das für Solosopran und zwei Solotenöre geschriebene „Et incarnatus est" im Credo (Seite 100), dann das Soloquartett im Benedictus (Seite 175) und schließlich das „Dona nobis pacem" des Agnus Dei (Wechselgesang zwischen Soloquartett und Chor), über welche Schubert die ganze Fülle seiner von Wohlklang beseelten Tonsprache ausgebreitet hat. Überhaupt ist dieses Werk eine Apotheose des schönen Klanges und darum typisch romantisch. Mit welch feinem Verständnis sind z. B. die Blechbläser behandelt, die in ihrer für damalige Zeiten starken Besetzung (2 Trompeten, 2 Hörner und 3 Posaunen) als ein selbständiger Klangkörper, reich an warmen und vollen Farben, einerseits der Gruppe der Holzbläser (2 Oboen, 2 Klarinetten und 2 Fagotten), andererseits den Streichern gegenübertreten. Dazu als vierte Gruppe der Chor, der hier Wirkungen aus seiner Klangfarbe erreicht, wie man sie bisher noch nicht gekannt hat. Hingewiesen sei hier nur auf das Andante con moto des Gloria: „Domine Deus, agnus Dei, qui tollis peccata mundi", wo die Tenöre und Bässe in Oktaven zu dem Fortissimo-Unisono des choralartigen Posaunenthemas treten und mit dem dumpf erbebenden Streichertremolo eine an mittelalterliche Askese gemahnende Stimmung hervorrufen, die noch durch die erschütternde Kontrastwirkung des im Pianissimo folgenden Chores erhöht wird. Hier offenbart sich wieder der Wille zu tonmalerischer Gestaltung, wobei sich dem Komponisten neben der reichhaltigen Palette des Instrumentalkörpers noch die Farbe einer Harmonik bietet, die in der damaligen Zeit unerhört stark gewirkt haben muß und noch heute Gewaltiges zu sagen vermag. Es sei hier nur hingewiesen auf die Folge terzverwandter Harmonien wie As-Dur und Ces-Dur in Takt 133 des Kyrie und die durch dynamische Kontrastwirkung verschärfte Folge von Es-Dur, H-Moll und G-Moll zu Beginn des Sanctus.

Erkennen wir in dem Hang zur Tonmalerei einen typisch romantischen Zug, so bietet sich uns in der Willkür, mit der Schubert in die Messe Prinzipien der absoluten Instrumentalformen verpflanzt, eine Erscheinung dar, die wohl aus dem Streben nach Verbreiterung der Form, keineswegs aber aus der inneren Entwicklung des Messetextes zu erklären sind. Ich meine hier die Wiederholung von Stimmungen, die längst überwunden sind, wie z. B. die nach dem „Passus et sepultus est" stattfindende Wiederholung des ganzen „Incarnatus" und „Crucifixus" (Seite 112 ff.). Ebensolche Willkür zeigt die Textbehandlung, bei der verschiedene Wörter, wie z. B. das „patrem omnipotentem" zu Beginn des Credos oder das zweite „Jesu Christe" im Gloria, überhaupt weggelassen wurden, während wiederum das „Osanna in excelsis" durch ein „Deo" verlängert erscheint.

So repräsentiert sich uns die Es-Dur-Messe als ein Werk, das zwar nicht von der tiefsten Auffassung des Messetextes durchdrungen ist, wie die Messen Bachs und Beethovens, wohl aber mit der ganzen naiven Frömmigkeit des schlichten, von tiefster Gläubigkeit erfüllten Gemütes zu uns spricht, das wir in Schuberts unvergänglicher Musik verehren und lieben.

Hermann Grabner.

Messe Nr. 6

I. Kyrie

Franz Schubert
1797-1828

2

le - - - i - son,

le - - i - - son,

le - - - i - son,

6

10

12

13

E. E. 4500

16

18

20

130

E. E. 4500

22

II. Gloria

28

30
Ob.
Cl.
Fg.
Cor. (B)
Tbe. (B)
Tbni.
Timp.
Vl.
Vla.
S.
da-mus te, be-ne-di-ci-mus te, lau-da - mus te, lau-da-mus te,
A.
T.
da-mus te, be-ne-di-ci-mus te, lau-da - mus te, lau-da-mus te,
B.
Vc. e Cb.

32

34

te, be-ne-di - ci-mus te, glo-ri-fi-ca - mus te, a-do-ra - mus

te, be-ne-di - ci-mus te, glo-ri-fi-ca - mus te, a-do-ra - mus

42

45

E. E. 4500

130
Ob.
Cl.
Fg.
Cor. (B)
Tbe. (B)
Tbni.
Timp.
Vl.
Vla.
S.
A.
T.
B.
Vc. e Cb.
cresc.
in ex - cel - sis De - o! Lau - da - mus
in ex - cel - sis De - o! Lau - da - mus

48

Andante con moto

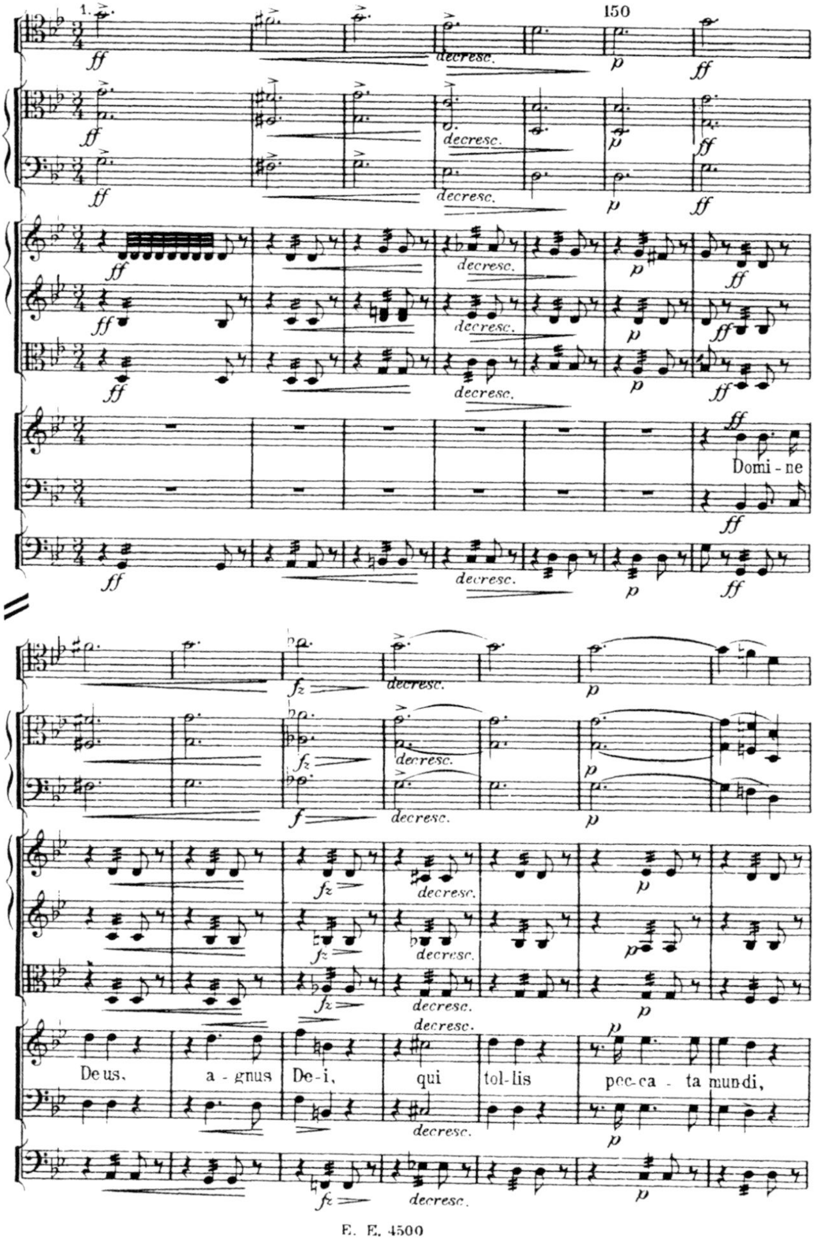

50

54

Tempo I.
Ob.
Cl.
Fg.
Cor. (B)
Tbe. (B)
Tbni.
Timp.
Vl.
Vla.
S.
Quo - ni - am tu so - lus sanctus, quo - ni - am tu so - lus san - ctus,
A.
quo
T.
Quo - ni - am tu so - lus sanctus, quo - ni - am tu so - lus san - ctus,
B.
Vc. e Cb.

Moderato

65

66

290 zu 2

E. E. 4500

68

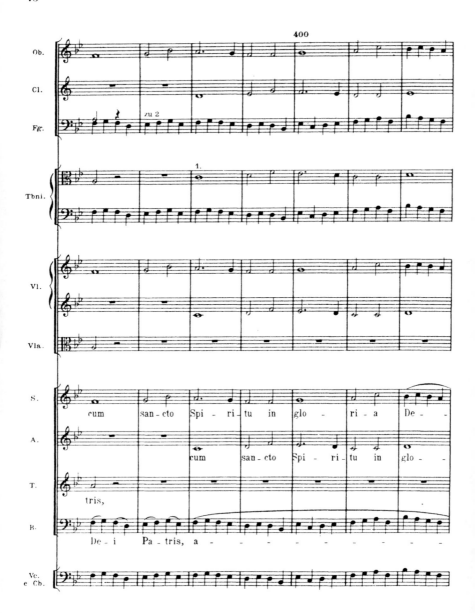

E. E. 4500

460

86

III. Credo

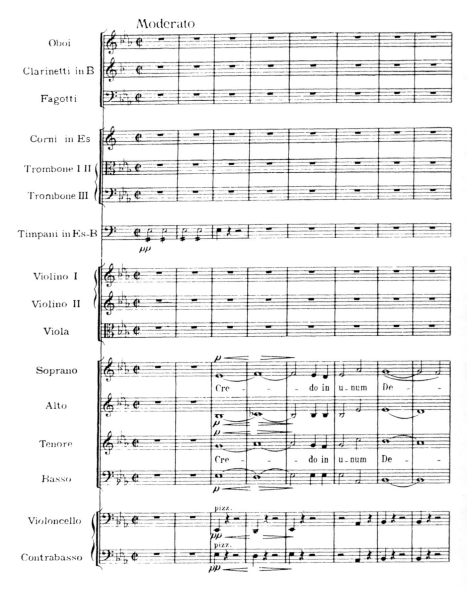

E. E. 1500

90

E. E. 4500

93

E. E. 4500

97

E. E. 4500

98

qui pro_pter nos ho _ mi _ nes et pro _ pter no_stram sa-

qui pro_pter nos ho _ mi _ nes et pro _ pter no_stram sa-

lu _ tem de _ scen _ dit, de _ scen _ dit de

lu _ tem de _ scen _ dit, de _ scen _ dit de

E. E. 4500

E. E. 4500

Andante

104

108

E. E. 4500

111

E. E. 4500

112

114

118

120

230
Ob.
Cl.
Fg.
Cor. (Es)
Tbe. (Es)
Tbni.
Vl.
Vla.
S.
A
T.
B.
Vc. e Cb.
cresc.
ff
i - te - rum ven - tu - rus est, ven - tu - rus est cum glo - ri - a,
ven - tu - rus est, ven - tu - rus est cum glo - ri - a, ju di-

126

128

340
Ob.
Cl.
Fg.
zu 2
Cor. (Es)
Tbe. (Es)
Tbni.
Timp.
Vl.
Vla.
S.
saecu-li, a - men, a - - - men, a - - - men, a -
A.
a - - - men, a - - - men, a - - - men, a -
T.
a - - - men, a - - men, a - - men,
B.
et vi-tam ven-tu - ri sae-cu - li, ven-tu-ri
Vo
Bassi

138

370

Ob.

Cl.

Fg.

Cor.
(Es)

Tbe.
(Es)

Tbni.

Timp.

Vl.

Vla.

S.

men, a - - - - - men, a - - - men,

A.

- men, a - - - - - men,

T.

- - - - - men, a - - men,

B.

- - - - - - - men,

Vc.
e Cb.

E. E. 4500

144

E. E. 4500

146

E. E. 4500

148

E. E. 4500

150

152

E. E. 4500

156

157

E. E. 4500

159

530

Ob.

Cl.

Fg.

Cor.
(Es)

Tbe.
(Es)

Tbni.

Timp.

Vl.

Vla.

S. men, a – – men, a – – – men.

A. men, a – – men, a – – men.

T. men, a – – men, a – – men.

B. men, a – – men, a – – men.

Vc.

Cb.

E. E. 4500

160

IV. Sanctus

E. E. 4500

162

E. E. 4500

164

168

Allegro, ma non troppo

174

V. Benedictus

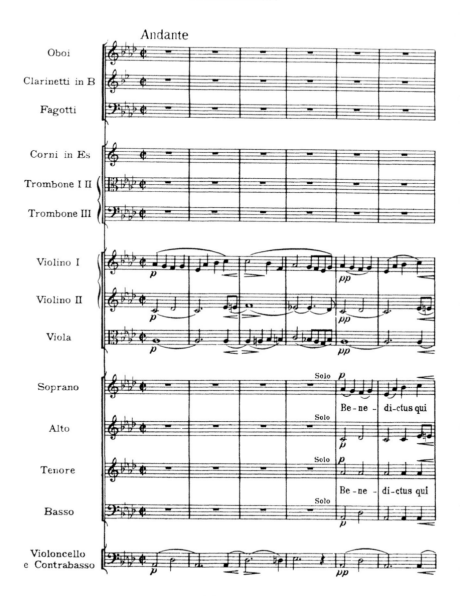

E. E. 4500

178

E. E. 4500

180

188

O sanna, dal segno ※
(Pag. 168)

E. E. 4500

VI. Agnus Dei

196

198

E. E. 4500

206

216

218

E. E. 4500

220

Allegro molto moderato

222

F. E. 4500

228

240

230